Piano Exam Pieces

ABRSM Grade 1

Selected from the 2015 & 2016 syllabus

MW00997398

Name

Date of exam

Contents

Editor for ABRSM: Richard Jones

Other pieces for Grade 1

First published in 2014 by ABRSM (Publishing) Ltd, a wholly owned subsidiary of ABRSM, 24 Portland Place, London W1B 1LU, United Kingdom © 2014 by The Associated Board of the Royal Schools of Music

Music origination by Julia Bovee
Cover by Kate Benjamin & Andy Potts
Printed in England by Headley Brothers Ltd, The Invicta Press, Ashford, Kent.

FSC
www.fsc.org
MIX
Paper from responsible sources
FSC™ C109619

A:1

Arietta

Lesson Five from Op. 42

Muzio Clementi
(1752–1832)

Muzio Clementi, an English composer of Italian birth, settled in London in 1774 and established a successful career as a pianist and teacher. His most important compositions are his keyboard works, which include about 70 solo sonatas as well as sonatinas and variations. During a continental tour as a solo pianist in the early 1780s, he stayed in Vienna for six months, taking part in a famous piano contest with Mozart. Afterwards, Mozart commented on his 'remarkable technique at the keyboard'. In 1798 Clementi established a firm in London that not only published music but also manufactured pianos.

Clementi wrote two influential educational works, the *Introduction to the Art of Playing on the Piano Forte* (London, 1801) and *Gradus ad Parnassum* (London, 1817–26). This Arietta is taken from a revised edition of the *Introduction*, published in 1826. The first phrase (bb. 1–4), from which the rest of the piece is derived, is not unlike a folksong in character. All slurs and dynamics are Clementi's own, except the hairpins in bb. 14–16, which are editorial suggestions only.

Source: *Eleventh Edition, with Great Improvements, of Clementi's Introduction to the Art of Playing on the Piano Forte*, Op. 42 (London: Clementi & Co., 1826)

Minuet in G

No. 2 from 12 Minuets, Hob. IX:3

Joseph Haydn
(1732–1809)

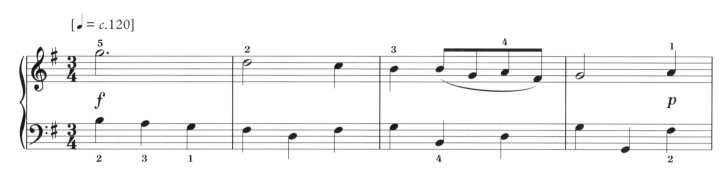

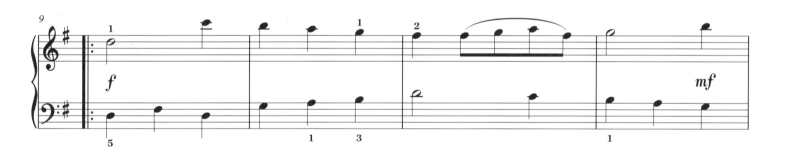

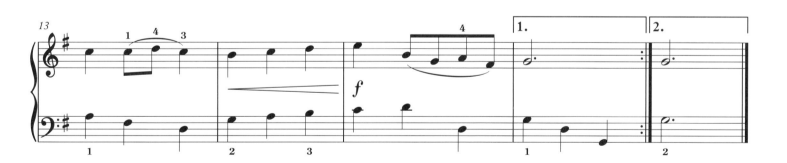

The great Austrian composer Joseph Haydn is noted for the inexhaustible variety of his treatment of the minuet, an elegant dance in moderate triple time, very popular throughout the 18th century. Haydn not only included minuets in his symphonies, but he also wrote over 100 separate orchestral minuets. Many of these, including the 12 Minuets of around 1763–7, from which this piece is selected, were later arranged by him for keyboard. Only the slur in b. 7 is original; all the others are editorial suggestions only, as are all the dynamics.
Source: autograph MS, Budapest, National Széchényi Museum (Esterházy-Archiv)

The Lincolnshire Poacher

Arranged by Hywel Davies

Trad. English

This piece is a modern piano arrangement of a traditional English song expressing a poacher's delight in his illicit activity. The song was first published in the late 18th century, and the first verse and refrain read:

> When I was bound apprentice, in famous Lincolnshire,
> Full well I served my master for more than seven year,
> Till I took up to poaching, as you shall quickly hear;
> *Oh! 'tis my delight on a shining night in the season of the year.*

Note that the first two left-hand notes are part of the melody, as shown by the dotted lines in bb. 2 and 14. This arrangement builds up to a pause chord at the start of the refrain (b. 12). Slowing down at b. 17 might suggest the poacher being more stealthy as the gamekeeper approaches, and then managing to escape after the pause in b. 18.

Das Schaukelpferd

from *Technik und Melodie*, Op. 228, Vol. 1

 B:1

Cornelius Gurlitt
(1820–1901)

Das Schaukelpferd The Rocking Horse

Cornelius Gurlitt was born in Altona, near Hamburg, and studied organ, piano and composition in Copenhagen. After travelling around Europe for some years, he settled in his native town, becoming organist of Altona Cathedral and professor at the Hamburg Conservatory. He composed over 200 works, including many small, attractive pieces for children. Typically, these are character-pieces with descriptive titles. In 'Das Schaukelpferd', the compound-time rhythms convey the rocking of the horse.

Source: *Technik und Melodie: Elementar-Klavierschule*, Op. 228, Heft I (Mainz and Leipzig: Schott, n.d.)

Løvet faller

from *Barnebilder*

Knut Nystedt
(born 1915)

Løvet faller Falling Leaves; **Barnebilder** Children's Pictures

The Norwegian composer Knut Nystedt was born in Oslo and studied organ, composition and conducting at the Oslo Conservatory. In 1947 he undertook further composition studies with Aaron Copland in the USA. He became organist and choirmaster at the Torshov Church, Oslo, in 1946 and a professor at the Oslo Conservatory in 1964.

Barnebilder, first published in 1952, is made up of ten easy character-pieces for children, each evoking something familiar from the child's world. The composer tells us that in 'Løvet faller' strict legato should be kept in both hands (this does not, of course, apply to b. 7).

El cant dels ocells

B:3

Arranged by Mark Marshall

Trad. Catalan

El cant dels ocells The Song of the Birds

This song, thought to date back to about 1600, comes from Catalonia – a principality that lies across the southern tip of France and north-eastern Spain – where the Catalan language is still spoken today. The words refer to Christmas, describing many different species of birds visiting the baby Jesus in his manger in Bethlehem. In modern times the carol has been revived in various arrangements, notably by the cellist Pablo Casals and the singer Joan Baez. In this piano arrangement, the birdsong is heard in bb. 7 and 14–16. The arranger, Mark Marshall, lives in Vivès – a village in French Catalonia.

The Giant's Coming

Stephen Clarke
(born 1964)

C:1

Stephen Clarke is a conductor, educator and composer. After a career conducting opera, he is now precentor (head of music) at Radley College, Oxfordshire. He has written about this piece: 'Having worked in theatres for 20 years before teaching, I really like dramatic music that paints a picture and tells a story, so I would perform this piece as if accompanying a scary children's cartoon.'

Calypso Joe

No. 9 from *Finger Jogging Boogie*

C:2

Stephen Duro
(born 1939)

Stephen Duro studied at the Royal College of Music, London, after which he read music at Cambridge University. In 1962 he travelled to Boston, Massachusetts, where he studied jazz and taught the piano, returning to England in 1966.

Duro's *Finger Jogging Boogie*, from which this piece is selected, is a collection of 17 pieces in lighter styles for the younger pianist. One of these styles is that of the calypso, a West Indian dance and song, chiefly from Trinidad. Calypsos were first sung by slaves on the plantations. Nowadays they often have topical texts, are frequently sung during the carnival and are played on steel pans. 'Calypso Joe' illustrates the jaunty, syncopated rhythms of this style of music.

C:3

Na krmítku

No. 19 from *Svět malých*

Petr Eben
(1929–2007)

Na krmítku Bird at the Feeding Box; **Svět malých** The World of Children

The Czech composer, pianist and organist Petr Eben studied piano and composition at the Prague Academy from 1948 to 1954. He then taught at Prague University (1955–90) and at the Academy where he had studied (1990–4). During the same period he also pursued a career as a concert pianist, travelling widely in Europe and America.

Svět malých, from which this piece is selected, consists of 20 little compositions for the piano. They are written in a contemporary idiom and have programmatic titles, which show the player how they should be characterized. 'Na krmítku' evokes the quick pecking of the bird as it feeds.